I don't like swimming

Written by
Miss Joyce

To the pupils of
St Cuthbert & The First Martyrs'
I hope you enjoy reading this book
about swimming.
Please keep on working hard.
Mrs Welsh
Swimming Teacher Oct 2022

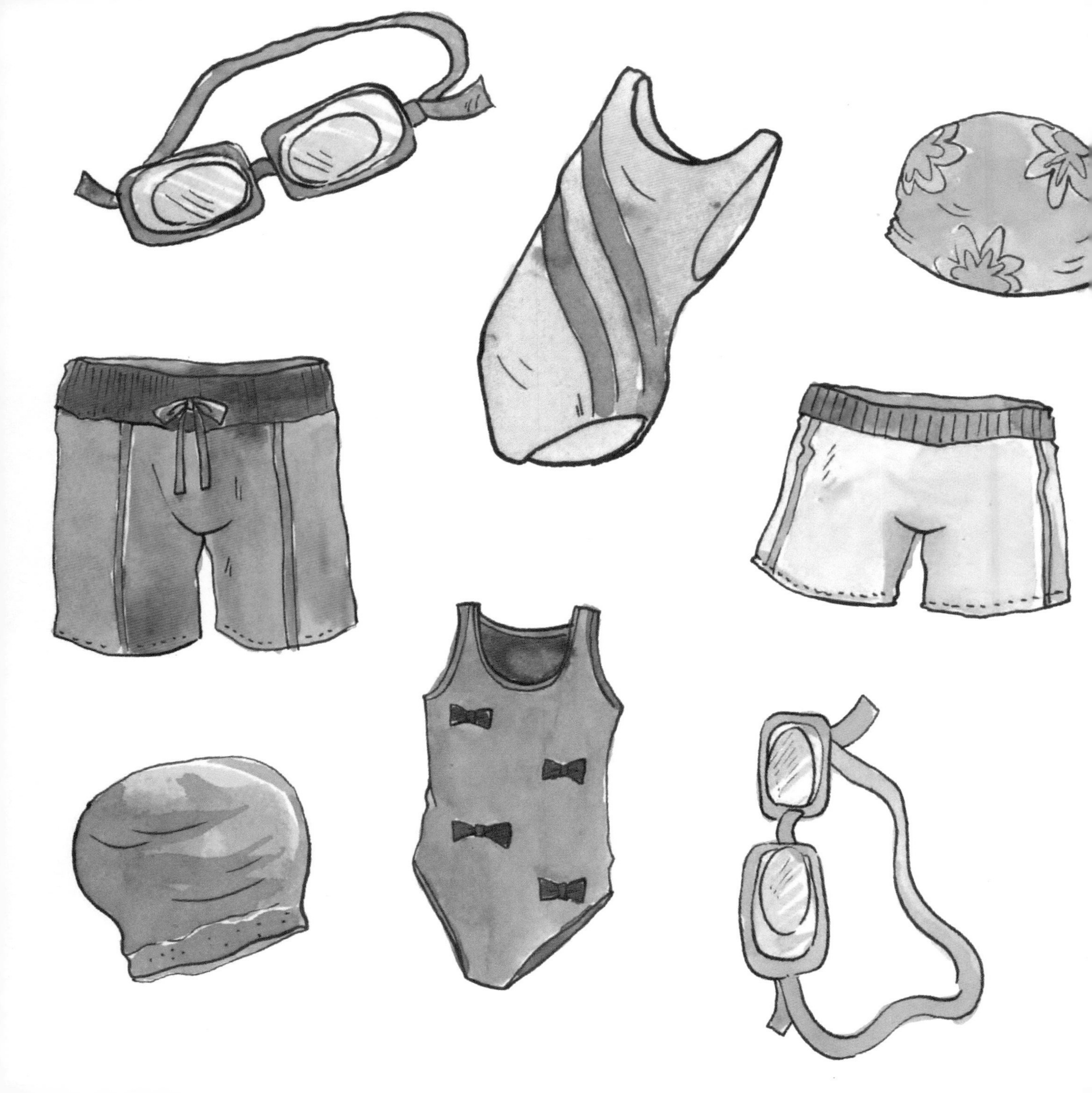

Jean-Paul does not like his swimming lessons.

His hat always hurts his head, and he always has water in his goggles.

Ezra
Isla
Mirella

Why do you think the children don't like their swimming lessons?

Point out all the things that look uncomfortable.

“I don’t want to wear my hat!” cried Ayala.

“It hurts because you haven’t put it on correctly,” pointed out Isla. “Look, if you use your fingers and thumbs, you can put your hat on more easily.”

Sla
AYALA

“Let me show you how,” said Mirella kindly. “You hold the hat just over your eyebrows with your fingers and thumbs and, with just one motion, we’re done. There you go!”

“Make sure you don’t push my ears down!” shouted Ayala. “It’s really uncomfortable and I won’t be able to hear the teacher!”

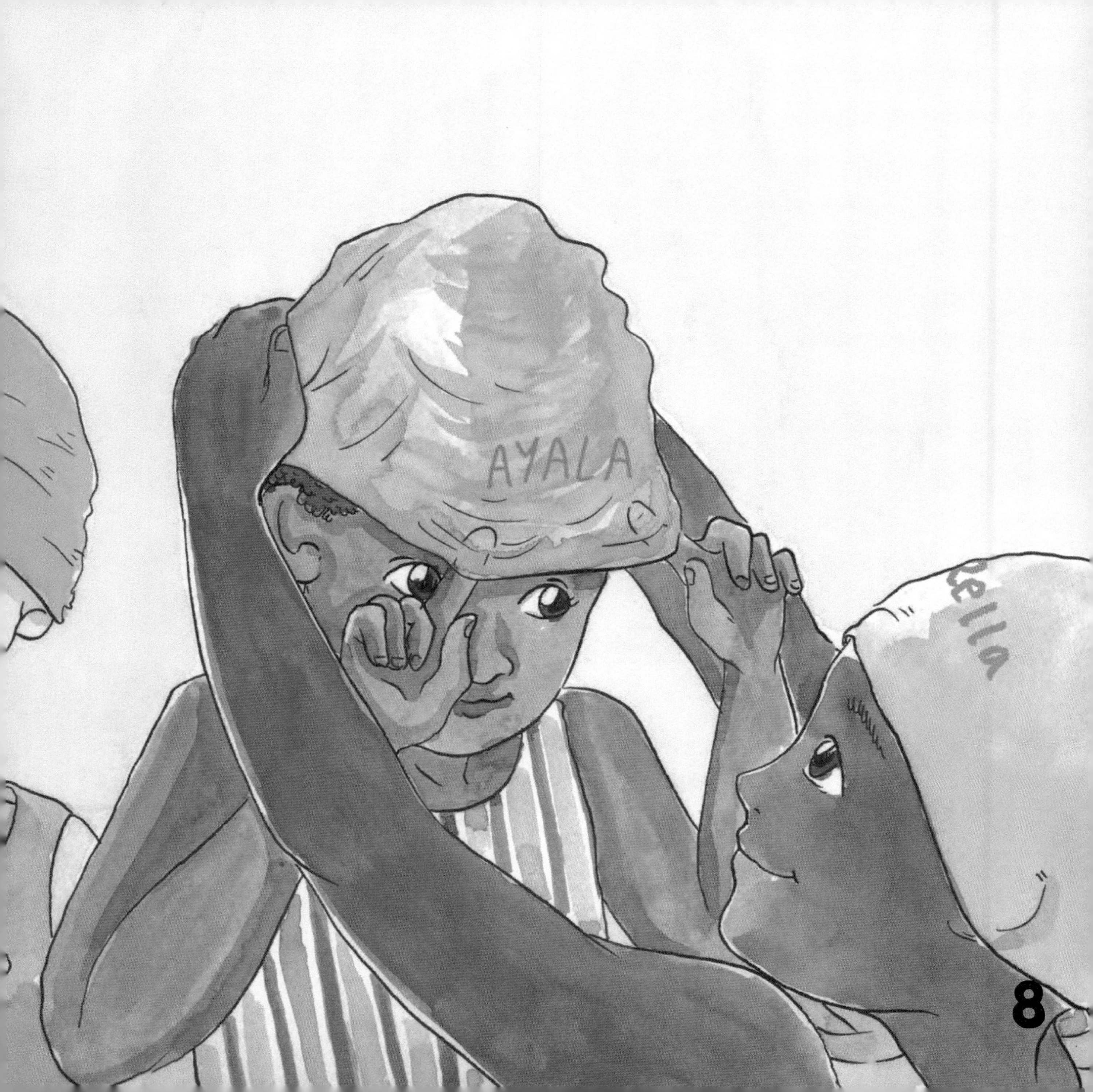
AYALA

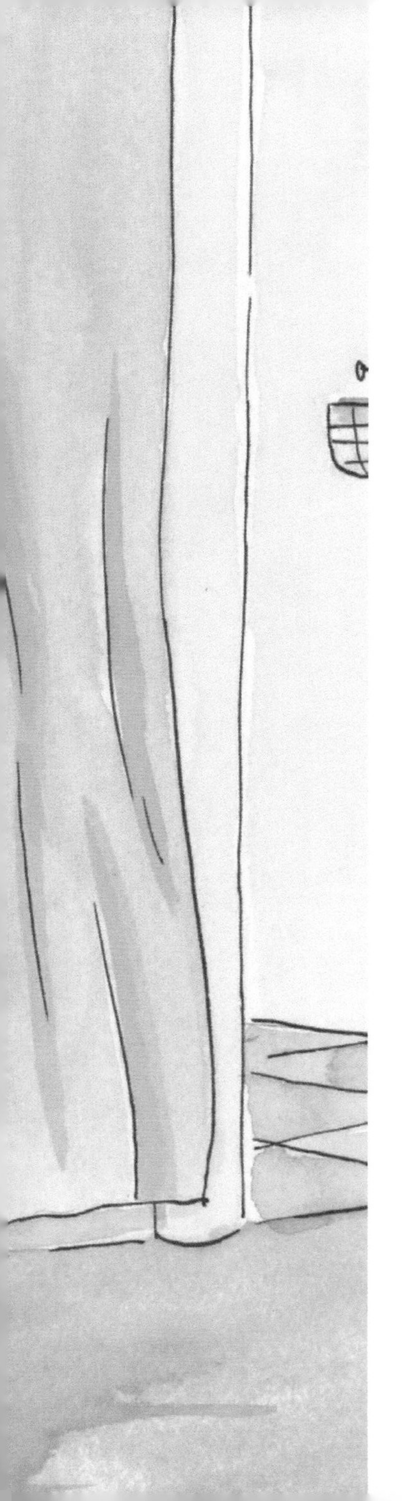

“My skin and hair get dry and itchy when I go swimming,” sighed Amelia.

It’s important that you wash your hair and body thoroughly after each lesson, especially if you have dry skin, dry hair, or both.

“There’s water in my goggles and my ears are pushed down!” cried Lucas unhappily.

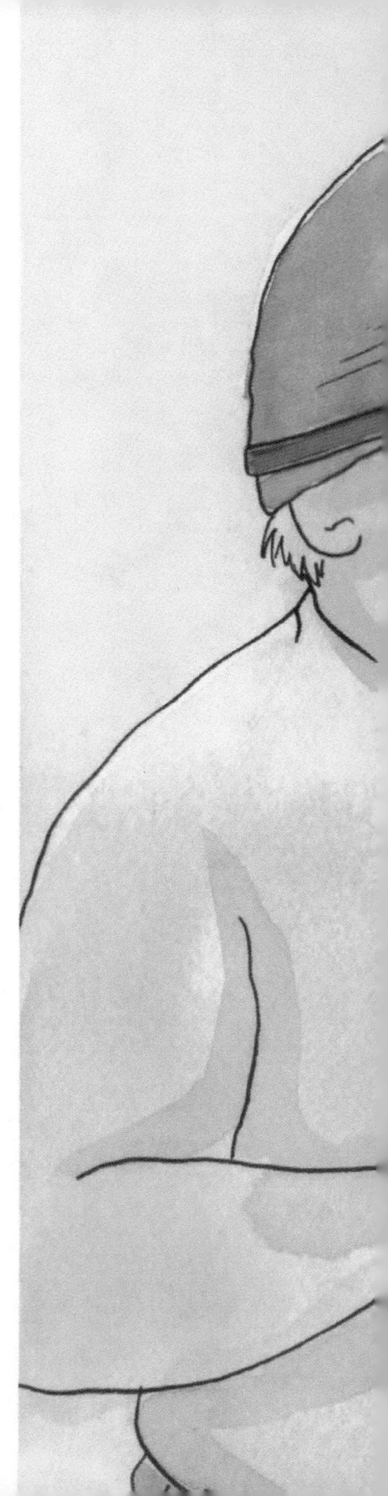

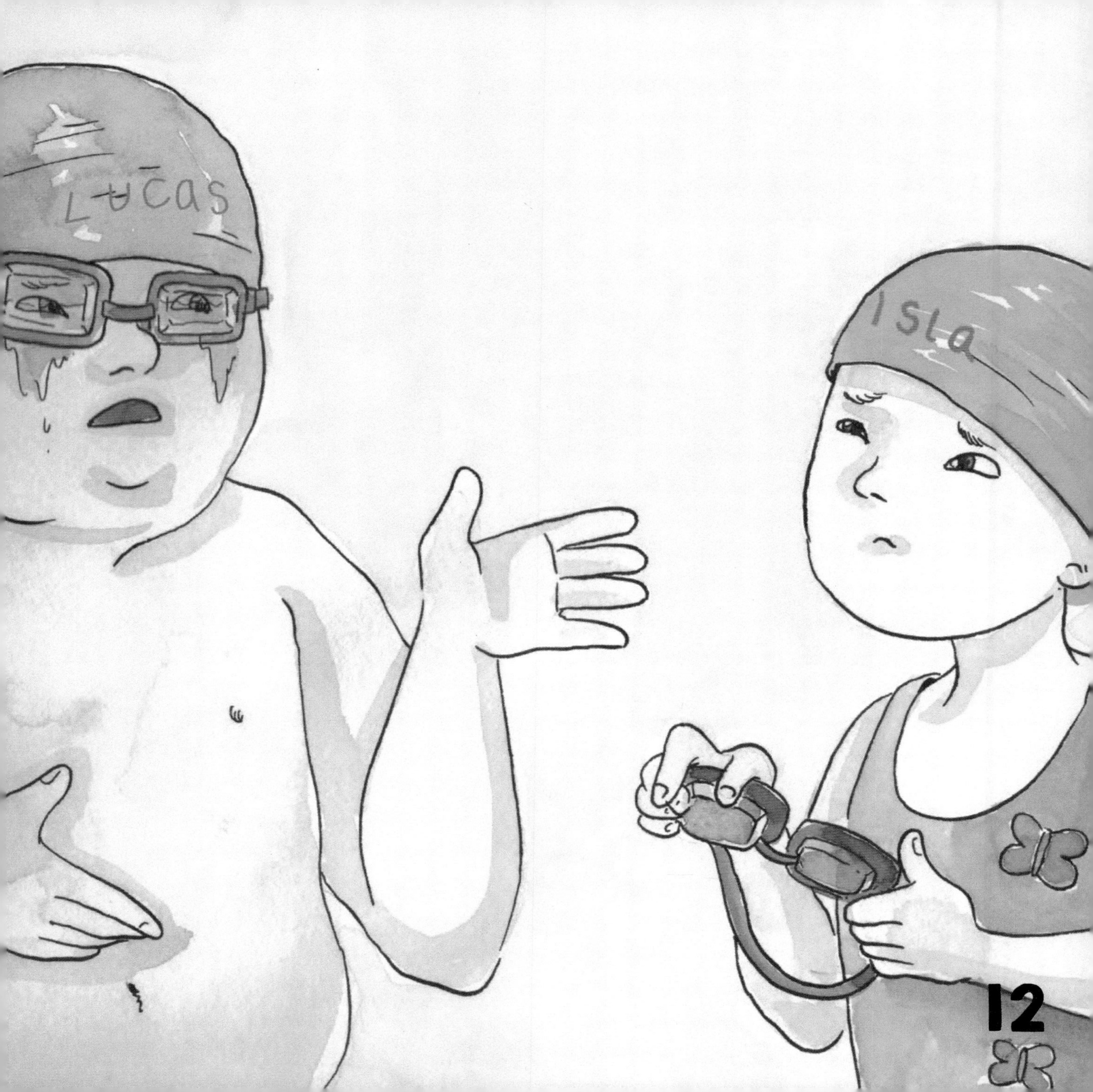
Lucas
Isla

Lucas
Emily

That's better.

Goggles need to be placed directly on your face, not on your hat!

"That's right," said Isla, "now I think we're all ready for our swimming lesson!"

STOP!!!

What do you need to do before you enter the swimming pool?

1. Go to the toilet!!!
"I don't feel like it," said Ayala.

"I think you should try anyway," said the teacher.

2. Blow your nose!!!
"My nose isn't running!" shouted Ayala.

"It's just to make sure that we don't pass on any germs to each other," explained the teacher.

3. Have a shower!!!
"But I had a shower this morning!" pointed out Ayala.

"You just need to rinse off the day's dirt to help keep the pool nice and clean," said the teacher.

AYALA
AYALA
AYALA

AMelia
AYALA

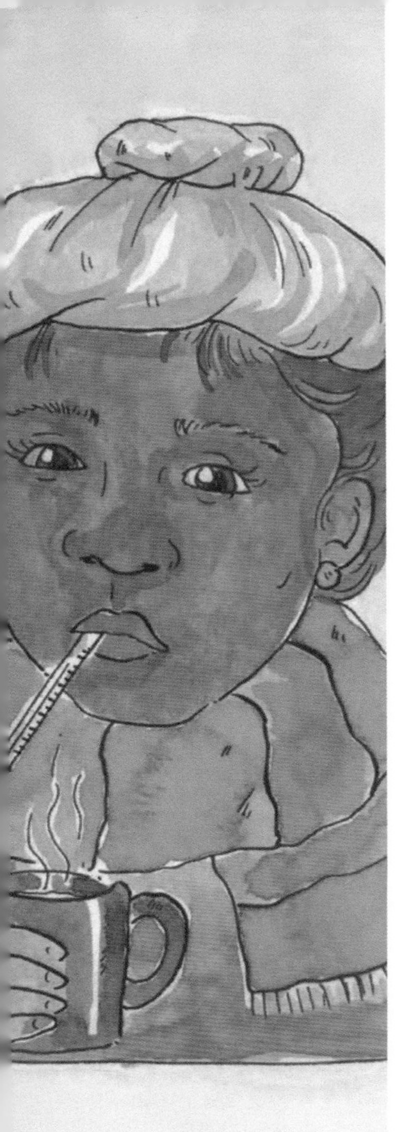

It's very important to help keep the swimming pool clean, which you can do by following these three simple rules.

If you don't follow these rules, you might spread germs, causing other people to get sick.

If you have a cold and sneeze in the pool, your friends or teacher could get sore eyes, an earache, or a sore throat and, potentially, miss lessons.

If your teacher gets sick you might have to have a cover teacher, or your lesson might get cancelled.

The average lesson is just 30 minutes long, so we need to make the most of every minute.

In order to make sure all of your lesson time can be used correctly, you shouldn't waste valuable time putting on hats and goggles or leaving to go to the shower or toilet.

Be prepared!!!

oLive

"We were all prepared and now we're ready for our swimming lesson!" shouted the children happily.

I LOVE
SWIMMING!

Read Book Two to see how Jean-Paul and his friends get on with their first swimming lesson.

It's an exciting time for the children as they can make new friends, find out how to use floats while blowing bubbles and, most importantly, have fun!

Come and share their first swimming adventure.

My first book is dedicated to the most important person in my life: my mother.

-

Acknowledgements:
To my mum, dad, and ALL of my family.
To all the managers at Balham Leisure Centre, who believed in me to run their swim programme for over twenty years. I would also like to thank the staff, who made my role so much easier. There are too many to mention. Thanks to Ashton, Dom, and Lucy from GLL.

Many thanks to Sarah-Leigh Wills for the wonderful illustrations, & Many thanks to J.C, S.F & S.J.M for the text.

Written by Miss Joyce
www.missjoyceswimming.co.uk

ISBN: 978-0-9955765-0-6

Illustration and Design by Sarah-Leigh Wills.
www.happydesigner.co.uk

Printed in Great Britain
by Amazon